BE THE VIP
WORKBOOK

CREATED BY
MATT MORSE

Mental Game VIP Workbook

Printed in the United States of America
Published by Compete Publishing

Author/Creator: Matt Morse

ISBN-13: 978-0-9969367-1-2

ABOUT THE CREATOR

Matt Morse is an entrepreneur, coach, consultant, author, speaker, and creator of Mental Game VIP. He is a former NCAA Division 1 student-athlete who trained extensively in the mental game during his baseball playing career at UAB. After having the opportunity to learn from and work alongside some of the best mental performance coaches in baseball, Matt had a vision of bringing them all together in an active research type project. As the process evolved, Mental Game VIP was built during Matt's senior season at the University of Alabama at Birmingham.

In addition to hosting, recording, transcribing, editing and sorting the interviews, Matt also designed the logo, built the website, and called the shots within his strategic social media marketing campaigns.

Due to NCAA Compliance restrictions, Matt was unable to promote Mental Game VIP using his name or likeness in any way until his NCAA eligibility was exhausted.

Matt's passion for the game of baseball and helping others become the best they can be on and off the field is strongly evident throughout his coaching and training of highly competitive athletes.

In addition to coaching, Matt also consults with and speaks to teams, organizations, coaches, and athletes around the world. For more information on Matt, to have him come speak to you and your team, or if you want to create your own VIP collection, visit **Matt-Morse.com** and follow @MattMorse_17 on Twitter!

CONTENTS

THIS BE THE VIP WORKBOOK BELONGS TO:

BE THE VIP DEFINED

The Mental Game VIP: Be The VIP Workbook gives you the opportunity to answer the same questions as the featured coaches in Mental Game VIP. You can embark on this VIP journey before, during, or after you get into the Mental Game VIP book and/or audio program. It is a great way to see where you are, what you've learned, and what you wish to use moving forward.

GameTime Q&A is a series of frequently asked questions among the baseball community. You will then be put on the **HotSeat**, where you can provide your initial thoughts on several popular topics. **The Closer** will give you the opportunity to provide recommended reading, anticipated insights on the future of the mental game and final comments.

The **Notes** section at the end can be used to take additional notes as you read/listen to the Mental Game VIP program. See where you stack up with the experts in Mental Game VIP with this Be The VIP Workbook!

WHAT IS THE MENTAL GAME?

_____

_____

_____

_____

_____

_____

_____

_____

_____

_____

_____

_____

_____

_____

_____

_____

_____

_____

EXCLUSIVE CONTENT & FREE RESOURCES

For additional content, audios, videos, links, training tools, social media and more, visit:

MentalGameVIP.com

GAME TIME
Q&A

PRE-GAME PREP FOR THE MIND & BODY

Many competitive baseball players participate in between 50-162+ games each year. What are some of the most effective techniques or routines to prepare the mind and body for competition on a daily basis?

_____

_____

_____

_____

_____

_____

_____

_____

_____

_____

_____

_____

_____

_____

_____

_____

_____

_____

IT'S ALL ABOUT YOUR PROCESS

In the game of baseball and life in general, there are so many external circumstances that are completely out of one's control such as what happens when the ball leaves your bat/hand, who is in the lineup, what the weather is like, who is watching you, etc... but we live in a society that is focused on results, batting average, ERA, etc. How does a player shift their focus to the process and the controllables?

CREATE FEELINGS OF FUN AND RELAXATION

A survey with some of the nation's best collegiate baseball players revealed that they perform at their best and experience their highest levels of success when they are relaxed and having fun. For most players, feeling relaxed and having fun follows success. How does a player create those feelings prior to having success?

CLEAR YOUR MIND

What are your best techniques to relax and clear your mind?

SLOW THE GAME DOWN & WIN THIS PITCH

In the heat of battle, how does a player slow the game down and get back to the present moment?

_____

_____

_____

_____

_____

_____

_____

_____

_____

_____

_____

_____

_____

_____

_____

_____

_____

_____

_____

THE 'IT' FACTOR

Some athletes just seem to have 'it'. What goes into the mind and makeup of the player who has that contagious personality that everyone loves to be around, that brings relentless positive energy every day and seems to be fueled by something much bigger than himself?

GET THAT NEGATIVE GUY TO BUY IN

Every team has 'that guy', the negative, closed-minded guy that is too cool to invest time into improving his mental game. How does a coach get that player to buy in to the system he is trying to implement?

CONSISTENT HIGH PERFORMANCE

What are the most important aspects to consistently performing at a high level?

_____

_____

_____

_____

_____

_____

_____

_____

_____

_____

_____

_____

_____

_____

_____

_____

_____

_____

_____

_____

POWER OF IMAGERY & MENTAL AT BATS

Can a player who is injured expedite the rehab process with imagery? Can a player who is not starting mentally prepare for when their time comes?

MAXIMIZE YOUR POTENTIAL UNDER PRESSURE

So many players underperform because they're afraid of failing. How do you effectively get them to perform to the best of their ability, meeting their full potential, with the potential of failure still lingering?

CHAMPIONSHIP CULTURE

What are the similarities among championship teams you have been around?

_____

_____

_____

_____

_____

_____

_____

_____

_____

_____

_____

_____

_____

_____

_____

_____

_____

_____

GET YOUR MIND RIGHT

What are some ways that coaches can be sure their players are in the proper mindset prior to competition?

_____

_____

_____

_____

_____

_____

_____

_____

_____

_____

_____

_____

_____

_____

_____

_____

_____

WIN THE BIG GAME

You hear about coaches and teams not being able to win the big game and then you hear about teams that are 'clutch' in the playoffs. What factors seem to contribute to these differences?

_____

_____

_____

_____

_____

_____

_____

_____

_____

_____

_____

_____

_____

_____

_____

_____

MENTAL TRAINING VS. PHYSICAL STRENGTH & CONDITIONING

Does mental training compare to physical strength & conditioning in the weight room?

GOAL-SETTING VS PROCESS

How important is goal-setting and envisioning the future in comparison to a focus on the process of doing what is most important today?

MILLION DOLLAR QUESTION

What do you know now that you wish you knew then?

HOT SEAT

Bringin' The Heat!

POSITIVE ENERGY

_____

_____

_____

_____

CONFIDENCE

_____

_____

_____

_____

CHAMPIONSHIP CULTURE

_____

_____

_____

_____

ROUTINES

_____

_____

_____

_____

PROCESS

_____

_____

_____

_____

CONTROLLABLES

_____

_____

_____

_____

MIND-BODY CONNECTION

_____

_____

_____

_____

SUCCESS

_____

_____

_____

_____

FAILURE

_____

_____

_____

_____

OMAHA

THE CLOSER

RECOMMENDED READING

What are the top books that a baseball player or coach must read?

_____

_____

_____

_____

_____

_____

_____

_____

_____

_____

_____

_____

_____

_____

THE FUTURE OF THE MENTAL GAME

As more and more people become educated on the importance of the mental game while technology continues to evolve, where do you see the future of mental training?

_____

_____

_____

_____

_____

_____

_____

_____

_____

_____

_____

_____

_____

FINAL THOUGHTS

Do you have any further advice for baseball players out there striving to improve their performance and get to the next level?

NOTES

_____

_____

_____

_____

_____

_____

_____

_____

_____

_____

_____

_____

_____

_____

_____

_____

_____

_____

_____

_____

_____

_____

_____

_____

_____

_____

_____

If you have had a positive experience with the *Mental Game VIP* Program and would like to share a testimonial to be featured in future editions, please e-mail Testimonials@MentalGameVIP.com

FOR MORE FROM MATT MORSE, VISIT <u>MATT-MORSE.COM</u>!

ADDITIONAL VIP RESOURCES

BEHIND THE SCENES WITH THE
TOP LEADERSHIP EXPERTS IN SPORTS

LeadershipVIP.com

EXCLUSIVE INTERVIEWS WITH
RON POLK
&
SKIP BERTMAN

MentalGameVIP.com/CoachingLegends

Made in the USA
Middletown, DE
12 January 2016